# THE LITTLE BOOK
# OF THE
# HIDDEN PEOPLE

ALDA SIGMUNDSDÓTTIR

# THE LITTLE BOOK OF THE HIDDEN PEOPLE

LITTLE BOOKS PUBLISHING

# TABLE OF CONTENTS

# Introduction

A few years ago, just after the Icelandic banks collapsed, there appeared in US magazine *Vanity Fair* an article about Iceland. Celebrated journalist and author Michael Lewis had visited to document the country's financial implosion, and while the main thrust of his piece had to do with the economy, he also made a wry reference to the Icelanders' belief in elves. Other international media outlets were quick to pick up the scent, including a reporter with a certain national broadcasting service, who called to ask if I would appear on an upcoming radio show about Iceland and elves. I told him I would be happy to; however, in the course of our conversation it became clear that he and I were not quite on the same page.

HIM: So Icelanders don't believe in elves any more?

ME: No. Hey. We're living in the 21st century.

HIM: But the *Vanity Fair* article said that they had to pause the construction of a big aluminum smelter until someone came in to check if there were elves living there.

ME: Er, *no*.

HIM: So *Vanity Fair* is lying?

ME: Maybe not *lying* but certainly misrepresenting the truth. What happened was that an archaeological survey was done to make sure that there were no important relics or ruins on the site that might be destroyed during the construction. Also, there was mapping done to see if the site had been mentioned in any old Icelandic folk stories. Stories that might or might not have involved elves. But to say that the construction was paused because elves lived on the site is completely ridiculous.

HIM: Oh.

He sounded so crestfallen that I almost felt sorry for him. Here he thought he had a delectable story, and some annoying person (me) had to go and ruin it. Still, he was a good sport about it, closing the conversation by saying that he still wanted me on the show since they would like to "present different points of view."

Two days later I received an email saying that, unfortunately, the plan now was to have only "experts" on the show, so my contribution would not be required. In the end, those experts were a) a professor of folkloristics at the University of Iceland, b) the owner of an "elf school," and c) an older gentleman who shared his experiences with elves as a boy. All of them emphasized that the belief in elves was alive and well in Iceland.

Sigh.

Before I go further, I should probably write a disclaimer: *there may be people in Iceland who still believe in elves*. In fact, while writing this book, one person told me about a friend of hers who still does. And let us not forget that man who runs the "elf school," or the woman who claims to be an elf seer and takes tourists around to show them where the elves live. I am going to give them the benefit of the doubt that they actually believe their own assertions and aren't just pretending to so they can rip off poor hapless tourists. However, those folks are the exception, rather than the rule. Personally I do not know anyone who believes in elves. And, in contrast to what is presented by the international media, we Icelanders do not go around talking to elves all day long, or refuse to build anything unless we've talked to them first.

By now you may have got the idea that I find this media elf fixation a tad annoying. And you would be right. It is not just because of the misrepresentation involved. It is because, taken out of its true context, the "elf belief" becomes a dumb parody of something quite profound. Iceland's elf folklore, at its core, reflects the plight of a nation living in abject poverty on the edge of the inhabitable world, and its people's heroic efforts to survive - physically, emotionally and spiritually. *That* is what the stories of the elves, or hidden people, are really about.

In the days when elf stories were alive and well in people's minds, life revolved around two basic needs: food and warmth. Neither of those was readily available. The Icelandic population lived in turf houses that were damp and crawling with bugs. Keeping the warm air *in* and cold air *out* was of paramount importance; hence there was a rather gruesome absence of ventilation. The *baðstofa*, a communal room in which people lived, slept, worked, ate, gave birth, died - where they played out their entire lives, basically - was frequently built over the animal shed for warmth. Lice were everywhere, and sometimes preyed upon people so severely that they had open lesions on their skin. Children had about a fifty-fifty chance of making it to adulthood. People were completely at the mercy of the elements - a bad summer could mean starvation, and one volcanic eruption could mean mass death. As if that were not enough, Iceland was a downtrodden and oppressed colony, subject to cruel, arbitrary laws and regulations imposed by its colonial masters and the church. In short: life was a bitch.

Under such soul-crushing conditions, and with no hope of marked improvement during their lifetime, how did people soldier on - year after year, decade after decade, even century after century?

The stories helped. A lot. They were the Icelanders' Prozac, providing refuge from the cruel circumstances people faced. They needed to escape from the harsh misery of their daily lives, so during those endless dark winter evenings, while they sat cooped up in the baðstofa and worked, they told each other stories. In some of the stories the hero took on formidable adversaries like trolls, ghosts or outlaws, and emerged victorious. In others a world existed parallel to their own, where there was not only prosperity, but also order. This was the world of the hidden people, which I believe was primarily a projection of the fervent dreams and desires of the human population.

The hidden people lived inside hillocks, cliffs or boulders, very close to the abodes of the humans. Their homes were furnished with fine, sumptuous objects. Their clothes were luxurious, their adornments beautiful. Their livestock was better and fatter, their sheep yielded more wool than regular sheep, their crops were more bounteous than those of the humans. They even had supernatural powers. They could make themselves visible or invisible at will, and they could see the future.

The hidden people themselves were also infinitely more attractive than regular mortals. These otherworldly beings were enveloped in an aura of glamour and mystique. They were tall, strong and regal. While often austere and demanding, they could also be gentle and kind. They were the elves in *The Lord of the Rings*, as opposed to the diminutive leprechauns from Irish mythology. Indeed, J.R. Tolkien is known to have been heavily influenced by Norse mythology and his idea of elves reportedly came from the Icelandic Eddas.

This projection of human desire was especially true when it came to the *ljúflingar* - hidden men who allegedly became the lovers of mortal women. Those stories doubtless reflected the deep yearning of mortal women for love and tenderness in the Iceland of old. It was something that was almost certainly lacking in their daily lives, not merely because toughness was considered a virtue, but because peasants in Iceland were forbidden to marry until they had reached a financial standing that hardly anyone could reach. If they did not marry, the reasoning went, they would not produce new mouths to feed. Yet the instincts have a tendency to override moral or legal decrees, and when they did, unwanted children tended to be the outcome. The parents of an illegitimate child could expect harsh sentences, so the stories of the ljúflingar could also have been made up to explain an accidental or unwanted pregnancy.

Yet hidden people were not only glamorous. They could also be wantonly cruel, pulling stunts like murdering people on Christmas or New Year's Eve for no good reason. In some stories they are portrayed as sexual predators. And they were powerful; they could make or break the fortunes of regular mortals. Often they came to people in dreams because they were in need of help. If the mortals cooperated with them, they were usually amply rewarded, enjoying good health, excellent crops and so on for the rest of their lives. Conversely, if they did not cooperate, or made the elves angry, something bad would inevitably befall them.

In that regard, elf stories were like morality tales. Yet on a deeper level, they might also have reflected people's yearning to have some control over their lives - something that was cruelly denied them otherwise, in almost every respect. As a peasant in the Iceland of old, you had the legal standing of a child. You were required by law to have a fixed place at a farm, where you were completely subservient to your employer-master. You could not as much as leave the farm to visit a friend or family member without his permission. If you were a woman, you received no salary for your work. Even if you were a step up from peasant status your world could change in an instant if, say, your spouse died - especially if you were a woman. Your household would be dissolved, your belongings auctioned off, and your children fostered out to whomever would take them. This was done even if you expressly wished to keep your family together and were fully capable of doing so.

And this is in addition to the Icelanders' utter defencelessness against the elements, on which I need not elaborate.

In short, those elf stories might have represented a vague yet desperate attempt at control: if you did the right thing and helped out a hidden person, then at least through your response you had a tiny bit of power over your own destiny.

In a category of their own were the tales of elves who abducted mortal children or lured away adolescents. Those may have reflected an even more grim reality: children and teenagers who routinely died or went missing. Partly this happened because the adults had to work constantly and could not always be on call to supervise. During the summers they often had to work some distance from the farm, and when they did they would leave their children unattended for longer or shorter periods. Any number of things could happen to those children. They might wander off somewhere, possibly falling into a river, off a cliff, or into a deep crevice in the landscape. Or maybe the children themselves were out working, with all the associated perils. As early as the age of five they were put to work watching the sheep, sometimes in a distant field. Imagine if a fog crept in and they tried to find their way home, only to become hopelessly lost. They could even have an accident, far from any available help. And so the bereaved parents, tormented by guilt, might conjure up a story in which their children had not, in fact, died, but had been taken away by elves who could provide a good life for them - even better than the one they themselves could have provided.

To the Icelanders, stories of elves and hidden people are an integral part of the cultural and psychological fabric of our nation. They are a part of our identity, a reflection of the struggles, hopes, resilience and endurance of our people. As such, they are very dear to us.

# A few more words about this book

Before going further, there are some things I should explain.

The terms "elves" and "hidden people" are used interchangeably, and mean the same thing. That is the way it is in Icelandic folklore, and I have kept it that way in the translation.

For each of the translated stories I have added commentary that ideally provides a fuller understanding of them, or at least some food for thought.

I have decided to keep the special Icelandic characters, such as *þ*, *ð* and *æ*, in the text rather than replacing them with the anglicized "th" or "d" or "ae". I hope you do not find that off-putting, even if the letters may seem unfamiliar. The key thing to remember is that þ is pronounced like a voiced "th" sound ("thespian"), ð is pronounced like a silent "th" sound ("this") and æ is pronounced "I".

I have translated most Icelandic words into English. If there are words in the original it is because they cannot be adequately translated, or have no equivalent in the English language. In the cases where I have not I have italicized the word the first time it appears in the book, but not after that.

An example of the above is the word baðstofa, literally "bath room." When Iceland was first settled it was overgrown with forest, so there was plenty of wood around. The homes of the settlers were relatively grand and had rooms for different purposes. One of those was this bath room, which today would likely be called a sauna, or steam room. As trees were systematically cut down for firewood or making coals, the forest did not have a chance to replenish itself, so wood naturally diminished. To make matters worse, the Little Ice Age set in, and Iceland turned colder than it had been before. Staying warm became paramount, and people gravitated towards the baðstofa, where the fire was perpetually burning. Over time this became the main room in the house, and though folks no longer took steam baths, the name stuck. The baðstofa became the room where everyone lived, worked, ate and slept, all huddled together for warmth.

The style of the stories in this book is very terse

and clipped. That is because they were originally oral narratives and were written down more or less verbatim. As a result they lack some of the details and descriptive language that modern readers may be used to. They also sometimes end rather abruptly. There are some odd, almost naive, turns of phrase, such as: "Then the elves murdered her," or "They walked until they reached a farmhouse - or so she thought, though it was actually a hillock." I have resisted the temptation to rewrite or embellish these because I feel that they are an integral part of the character of the tales.

You may notice some common motifs or themes in the stories. This, too, is a result of their oral transmission. As stories were passed from person to person they naturally changed. Details were omitted or added, stories knitted together, and so on. I like to think of them as being similar to Chinese Whispers, a game in which one person whispers a word to the next in a circle and by the time it gets to the end it is either a completely different word, or substantially changed. I have included some such stories in this book, most notably the two versions of the story about the woman in the mountain dairy.

Of a similar nature were stories that were known in more than one geographical region, but took on the specific characteristics of the area in which they were being told. A good example is "On the origins of the hidden people," which is strikingly similar to a German folk tale. However, instead of Eve's dirty children becoming permanently hidden, as in the Icelandic version, they became peasants in the German version, and the clean and presentable children became royalty.

In the 17th and 18th centuries, Iceland's stories of hidden people and outlaws began to merge. I am not entirely sure why, save for the reason given above - stories unwittingly being knitted together in the oral transmission. (The expert I contacted on the subject did not have any theories either.) Perhaps it was because outlaws were regarded with a certain fear and reverence, similar to the hidden people. They were individuals who had committed a crime and had been banished from regular society as a result. An excellent example of such a story is "The outlaw on Kiðuvallafjall mountain." In it, an outlaw lives in a boulder and appears to a mortal man in a dream. Both of these motifs are characteristic of hidden people stories. He entreats the man to help him in his hour of need, which ... well, I won't spoil it for you, and instead refer you to the notes at the end of the story. Incidentally, that particular story is also included in my *Icelandic Folk Legends* collection, but I wanted to include it here as well, as it illustrates so well what I mention above.

A few words about the collecting of the stories.

Like folk tales everywhere, the ones in this book were not considered particularly significant or important until the mid-nineteenth century. At that time there was a nationalistic revival in Europe and one of its manifestations was that folk tales, folklore, old customs and the like, previously disregarded as primitive and backward, began to be seen as unique reflections of their particular cultures. People began collecting oral narratives and writing them down, the most renowned being Jacob and Wilhelm Grimm with their *Grimm's Fairy Tales*.

In Iceland, two men, Jón Árnason and Magnús Grímsson, initiated the collection and recording of Icelandic folk stories. The first published collection of these appeared in 1852, to a lukewarm reception. Only when a German scholar, Konrad Maurer, came to Iceland a few years later and also collected stories were Árnason and Grímsson's efforts recognized. Maurer's collection, *Isländische Volkssagen der Gegenwart*, was published in Leipzig in 1860, and subsequently Árnason and Grímsson's collection was also published in Germany. Grímsson passed away in 1860 but Jón Árnason continued to collect stories over the ensuing years. Yet not until almost a century later did their collected stories appear in print in Iceland. The stories in this book are taken from that collection, known as *Íslenzkar Þjóðsögur og Æfintýri*, or Icelandic Folk Tales and Legends.

Finally, I should stress that the observations in this book are largely my own personal reflections. Some of them are recognized in academic circles, such as the theory of the stories being the anti-depressants of the day, while others are my own personal musings and should not be taken as absolute truths. If you are interested in learning more about the Icelanders of yore, do check out my *Little Book of the Icelanders in the Old Days*, which is entirely devoted to life in Iceland in centuries past.

And now, on to the stories.

# On the origins of the hidden people

Once upon a time, God asked Eve, the mother of all living, to show him her children. He told her to have them ready at a specific time and place, washed and freshly combed, and as well dressed as possible.

Eve was happy to comply with God's wishes, but because she had so many children she did not want to spend time getting them all ready. So she chose a few of each gender that she considered less presentable than the others and hid them in a cave. She closed the entrance to the cave so that they could not escape, and took the others to be inspected by God.

Seeing her children, God asked Eve if there were any more. Eve replied that there were not.

God said: "Those that you want to hide from your God will henceforth be hidden from you, your husband and all your descendants, except those that I choose to be exempt. From this day on they shall be of no use to you, nor shall they give you any enjoyment."

# The ways of the hidden people

It is said that the government and religious customs of the hidden people are similar to those that were common here [in Iceland] in the past. Often the locations of their churches are specified. People have said that they came to their church doors and heard the old Lutheran church songs being sung, and sermons being given in accordance with the Lutheran faith.

They have marketplaces. One of those is said to be a large rock named Snasi that extends into the sea from the peninsula between Berufjörður and Króksfjörður in Reyhólasveit district. Still, this does not prevent them from going to the marketplaces of our merchants and taking from them whatever they wish.

I have not heard of them owning livestock, other than horses and cows. The cows are said to be excellent milkers and are therefore great assets. Sometimes the cows came into the possession of humans if they were injured to the point of bleeding. The hidden people no longer wanted them after that.

They tend to abduct babies that have not yet been baptized and to replace them with wrinkly old people disguised as infants. These are called changelings. Consequently children should not be left alone, and never if the sign of the cross has not been made over them beforehand. To make the hidden people return the infants and take back the changelings, the changelings must be flogged without mercy.

Hidden women often charm adolescents into thinking that they are their mothers or foster mothers. The adolescents then follow them into boulders, up to the mountains, and so on, where they are later found, deeply disturbed. Many such cases have been reported.

There are numerous stories of elf men or women being sighted, and of people hearing the sound of a butter churner, a jangling of keys, or similar. Lights and such have been seen inside boulders and cliffs. All this is confirmed by numerous witnesses who say they have both heard and seen these things. Attempting to disprove this folly with reasonable arguments only makes things worse, for you will then be accused of belittling honourable men, as well as your ancestors and relatives, and turning them into liars. By doing so you will also be doubting the omnipotence and wisdom of

The Creator, who, as the old ministers used to say, "has such a lot in his pantry."

Existence of the hidden people can be proven through tangible objects: chests, scarves, rings, key rings, swaddle cloths, chalices with black marks in the bottom, the fine green and red garments that my grandmother saw at her great-grandmother's, or at the home of the minister's wife, or that my mother heard her grandmother say that her foster mother had seen in such vast abundance.

Their homes are a cut above those of the mortals. Midwives have seen the inside of them, as hidden women can only give birth if mortals lay hands on them - in some cases, at least. Mortals can also be physically attracted to hidden people. Unfortunately, sexual relations with them end badly in most cases.

Only those who are clairvoyant can see hidden people, except when the hidden people choose to reveal themselves. Being clairvoyant means that the baptism water did not enter your eyes properly when you were baptised as a child.

Hidden people change residence on New Year's Eve. They move in convoys, and the women of mortal households set aside meat and various delicacies for them to take. Sometimes mortal women enter the hillocks with them, if they are friends. It is also a custom of mortal women to circle their own homesteads on foot while speaking these words: "Come all who wish to come, leave all who wish to leave; it will not harm me or my people."

On New Year's Eve, folks were told to lie down at the intersection of two roads and to stare at the edge of a razor-sharp axe. They were not to speak a word, no matter what was said to them, for if they answered, they went insane. If they managed to stay silent, on the other hand, they became tremendously wise.

The reason why there are so few elf sightings now is that, since awareness of their existence grew, they have relocated to Finnmark.

There are stories of elf convoys that travelled into towns during the summer, and of funeral processions with the widow or widower following along behind. Some report psalms being sung, yet with the psalm beginning at the ending and progressing in reverse. There are stories of light being carried from one place to another, and strange boys and men who helped mortals round up sheep, yet did not speak a word. They then vanished when they were sought, or when people took a break from working.

The grandmothers of the mothers now alive claimed to have assisted hidden women in childbirth. They also spoke of jugs that appeared out of nowhere, of filling them with milk, and of the jugs just as mysteriously disappearing. One positive aspect of their interaction with elves was that, when their cows came into heat, the women only had to lead them out into a snowstorm for them to become pregnant. Then, at the end of the gestation period, their cows would give birth to calves with no tails.

Hidden people are said to have given food to the hungry. The only catch was that the food had to be consumed in full - if there was any left over, or if the food was not accepted, it would bring bad luck.

When the Reverend Einar in Eydalir was a boy he said that he went with a farm labourer who disappeared every Christmas to a hillock, or what looked like a farm. Everything there was clean and tidy. They found two women inside, one of them older than the other. The farm labourer had sexual relations with her, whereas the boy did not want to have sexual relations with the other. At this the women are said to have become angry, but because of the farm worker's relationship with the older woman the boy was given the choice of having bad fortune in his life when it came to his farming activities, or with regards to his children. He is reported to have chosen the former.

*This text was slightly edited from the original, for the sake of relevance and clarity.*

## NOTES

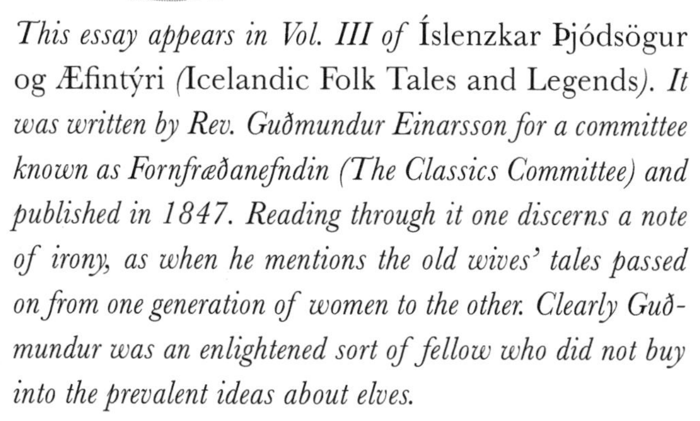

*This essay appears in Vol. III of* Íslenzkar Þjódsögur og Æfintýri (Icelandic Folk Tales and Legends). *It was written by Rev. Guðmundur Einarsson for a committee known as Fornfræðanefndin (The Classics Committee) and published in 1847. Reading through it one discerns a note of irony, as when he mentions the old wives' tales passed on from one generation of women to the other. Clearly Guðmundur was an enlightened sort of fellow who did not buy into the prevalent ideas about elves.*

*This essay also presents us with the most bizarre idiom that I believe I have ever come across in Icelandic: "[He] has such a lot in his pantry." I am not sure what it means, though am guessing something along the lines of "a lot on his plate."*

*The belief in those days was that everyone was born with the ability to see the hidden people, but when the baptism water entered people's eyes, they lost that ability. Not seeing was a good thing, because if you were able to see hidden people you were also vulnerable to their machinations. If a child was abducted or lured away by a hidden person, the blame was usually put on the minister who had baptized the child since apparently he had not done a proper job of getting the water into its eyes.*

*I find this concept of "not seeing" fascinating. It is sort of like "hear no evil, see no evil, speak no evil" being hailed as a great virtue. I have to wonder if this was yet another coping strategy for the Icelanders of old, since "seeing the light" with regards to their own oppression was so dangerous and terrifying.*

# The elf adornment

Once in bygone days, all the people from a certain farm went to evensong on New Year's Eve, save for one maidservant who was made to stay at home to watch over the farm.

Soon after everyone had left, the maidservant heard a commotion and then a knocking at the door. She took a light and went to answer it, and found outside a large group of hidden men and women who invited her to dance with them, which she gratefully accepted. After she had danced for a while, the elves murdered her. She lay dead in the doorway when the other farm residents came home from church.

The same incident repeated itself the following New Year's Eve. All the farm residents went to church, except for one maidservant who remained at home. After a time she heard a great ruckus, as the other maidservant had. There was a pounding at the door, and outside she found the same visitors as had been there the previous New Years' Eve. The elves were boisterous in the extreme, and with much glee invited the maiden to dance with them. This ended with the hidden people cutting off her head on the farmhouse threshold, and that is how the farm residents found her when they returned from church.

On the third New Year's Eve, everyone left the farm as before, except for one maidservant. When the people had gone she swept the floor and placed lights throughout the house wherever possible. Then she sat down to read. After a while she began to hear loud noises and a strange commotion. There was a knocking at the door, but she ignored it and continued reading.

Next the elves came into the baðstofa and tried to entice her to dance. She ignored them. They greatly admired how tidy everything was, and also the determination with which she read her book.

The elves passed the night in the baðstofa, engaged in frenzied dancing. When dawn finally came the maidservant said: "Thank God it is daybreak." This so shocked the elves that they instantly made to leave. Before going, one of the hidden men placed a chest on the floor, which he asked the maiden to accept. He told her that she should use the adornment contained within it on her wedding day. The elves then vanished and the maiden kept the chest, telling no one of its existence.

A short while later the farm residents returned and were greatly relieved to find the maidservant safe and sound, even if the house was bedlam from the carousing of the elves.

Much later, when the maidservant was preparing to wed, she opened the chest as the elves had instructed and found a woman's dress sewn with gold thread, and a gold ring. She is said to have been exceptionally beautiful in her elf adornment.

## NOTES

*From approximately 1300 onward, Icelandic authorities - meaning the church and king - took great pains to ban dancing among the Icelanders. Dancing, they believed, lowered people's inhibitions and led to all sorts of debauchery, which in the eyes of the authorities was synonymous with unwanted pregnancies. Those had to be avoided at all costs, for the simple reason that there was not enough food to feed everyone already in the world.*

*Before the ban, dances were among the few opportunities people had to get together and have some fun. One of the most infamous was the Jörfagleði, an annual dance held at the farm Jörfi in Haukadalur. One year, nineteen children are said to have been conceived there, while other reports put that number as high as thirty.*

*After a couple of centuries of feeble prohibitions, dancing was unequivocally outlawed in Iceland from the early 1700s until the late 1800s. My thought is that stories like this one may have been "floated out there" to warn against the evils of dancing. The propaganda of the day, if you will.*

*Incidentally, the man who finally succeeded in banning the Jörfagleði events, Jón Magnússon, fell on some seriously hard times after that. He was the local district magistrate and was eventually tried for a variety of crimes, evicted from office, and just barely escaped flogging and execution. He died in complete poverty. The word on the street was that his misfortune was a direct result of the Jörfagleði ban, since he had upset the elves who routinely took part in the celebration. In the end, the story went, the elves had taken a stand with the proletariat against the ruling elite. So in other words the elves were not only enchanting, glamorous and powerful, they were also political.*

# An elf woman in distress

In the east - it is said to have been in Oddi - a girl was fetching laundry in the churchyard one evening when she was approached by a man whom she did not know. He took her by the hand and asked her to come with him, saying that no harm would come to her, "... but if you do not come you will experience a change in your fortune." The girl did not dare refuse him, and so complied. They walked until they reached a farmhouse - or so she thought, though it was actually a hillock. They went to the door and he led her inside through a long tunnel, until they came to the baðstofa. It was dark at one end, and there was a light burning at the other. A woman lay on the floor moaning, clearly in distress as she struggled to give birth. An old woman, deeply troubled, sat next to her. The man who had brought the girl now spoke: "Go and help my wife so that she can give birth to the child."

The older woman left the room, and the girl went to where the woman lay on the floor. She laid hands on her, as she felt was needed. The woman was soon out of danger, and the child was born. Its father immediately came over with a glass jar and asked the girl to apply some of its contents to the child's eyes. She did as instructed, then swiped her finger across one of her own eyes. Instantly with that eye she could see many people at the other end of the baðstofa. The man came over, took the jar from her, and left the room. On returning, he thanked her for her help, as did the old woman. They told her that she would enjoy good fortune in her life from then on. The man then gave her cloth from which to make an apron, of a kind that she had never seen. He took her hand and led her back to the churchyard where she had first encountered him. Then he left, and she went back home.

The following winter the wife of the district minister died, and this girl became his new wife. She often said that she saw hidden people. When, for instance, she observed them gathering up their hay, she had her own hay gathered up as well. Usually it would begin to rain soon afterwards, even though the sky had been clear moments before.

One time she went to town with her husband, the minister. While in the shop she happened to see the hidden man carrying his purchases away from a hidden merchant who was there. She made the mistake of addressing him with these words: "Greetings friend, and thank you for the last time we met." At that he walked over to her, brought his finger briefly to his mouth, and swiped it across her eye. This startled her, and after that she never again saw the hidden people or anything they did.

## NOTES

*At the start of this story we have a girl gathering up laundry in the churchyard. If you are like me you might have scratched your head over that one. Laundry in a churchyard?* Really?

*Apparently in the old days, churchyards were pretty popular places in which to dry the laundry. No doubt because there were not many things that could serve as clothes lines back then. Trees and bushes, though relatively common in inhabited areas today, were probably rather scarce. So crosses and railings around graves undoubtedly came in handy for laying things out to dry, and that is what people did. This practice became so common that eventually a law was expressly passed prohibiting folks from laying their laundry out to dry in the churchyard.*

*Now to the "elf woman in distress," which is probably the most ubiquitous theme in all elf stories. This one, as many others do, demonstrates just how insistent the elves could be if they wanted something. They rarely asked nicely. It was always:* Do as I ask or regret it for the rest of your life. *Paraphrased:* I am not asking.

*I cannot leave off without mentioning the phrase "Thank you for the last time [we met]." Anyone who moves to Iceland soon learns this idiom. It's what Icelanders say to each other when they meet up after an interval, especially if they had a particularly enjoyable or memorable time the last time they got together. Though sometimes - as in this case - it is better to keep your mouth shut about it.*

# Father of eighteen in the elf world

It happened one summer that all the residents of a particular farm were out working in the fields, except the mistress of the house, who had stayed at home with her young son. He was two or three years old at the time, had already learned to talk, and was generally considered to be a very intelligent, promising child.

The woman had to go and wash the milk troughs in a brook close to the farm, and left the boy on his own while she was gone. She parted with him in the doorway of the house, and returned a short while later. The moment she spoke to him he began to howl most wretchedly, such as she had never heard before. She was extremely startled, as the child had always been calm, gentle and obedient. Now the only sounds that came from him were dreadful shrieks and wails.

Time passed, and the boy never spoke a word. He was clamorous and obstinate, had stopped growing, and generally behaved in a completely nonsensical manner. His mother had no idea how to manage his behavior and grew quite desperate. Finally she decided to visit a neighbour who was renowned for her wisdom and common sense. When she had told her about her child's awful transformation, her neighbour asked how long it had been since the change took place and how she thought it might have come about. The mother related the full story, sparing no detail.

Her neighbour then asked if she thought the boy might be a changeling. "I believe he might have been exchanged when you left him there in the doorway."

"I don't know," said the mother. "How can I find out the truth?"

"Leave him on his own, and let him come upon some strange sight," replied the neighbour. "He will speak if he believes he is alone, and you should eavesdrop on what he says. If it is something odd or alarming, then flog him without respite until something happens."

The boy's mother thanked her friend for the advice and went home. Once there she took out a small pot and placed it in the middle of the kitchen floor. She took several broomsticks and tied them together so that they reached the chimney. At one end she tied a wooden spoon that she made sure was sticking out of the pot.

Next she fetched the boy and left him in the kitchen by himself, remaining just out of sight, but within earshot. After a few moments the boy began to circle the pot, examining it and the wooden contraption that jutted out of it. Finally he said: "I am old as my whiskers show - a father of eighteen in the elf world - yet never have I seen such a long spoon in such a small pot."

At this the woman strode into the kitchen, seized the changeling, and began flogging him hard with brushwood branches while he shrieked like mad. After a good while, a strange woman entered the kitchen. She held a young boy, fair and lovely, on her arm, whom she treated with affection. To the mistress of the house she said: "See how we differ in our ways: I rock your child while you flog my husband." She then put the boy down and led her husband away, both of them vanishing. The young boy, meanwhile, grew up in his mother's care, and became a fine adult.

## NOTES

*As we have established, many of the old folk tales were clearly designed to send messages about something. Here, presumably, the message is that terrible things can happen if you leave your child alone. For instance an elf might come into your house and put her decrepit old husband who does nothing but howl all day long in your child's place, after making him look exactly like your child so you can't tell the difference.* Remember that.

*Meanwhile, I have been pondering the significance of this "old people" business. I mean, why decrepit* old *people? Then one evening I was watching a telethon for UNICEF, where they were showing images of all these starving, malnourished children. They were so small, yet their faces looked* so old. *Like they had aged a lifetime from all that suffering. And it made me think. Were the children in Iceland back in the day also so malnourished that they looked old before they were even past infancy? The thought was rather disturbing, as was the idea that those children would be flogged mercilessly until "something happened."* Something. *But what if nothing happened? What if they were starving, malnourished children, and were flogged mercilessly because someone thought they were changelings?*

*It hardly bears thinking about.*

# The elf confirmation

At Móafell in Fljót district there once lived a widow whose name was Anna. She had two daughters and a son named Jón, who had a feeble mind and a weak constitution.

When the girls were sixteen and seventeen and Jón thirteen, the sisters went to gather herbs and grasses in Móafellsdalur valley. It was autumn, and the day was foggy. Around midday they were in a field just east of the river when they saw two girls gathering herbs in another field. Soon they met up, and the Móafell sisters realized that the other girls were strangers. They asked them where they lived, to which they replied that they did not live far away. Still, they would not give their names, nor the location of their home.

The four of them chatted about various things, and the two girls asked the sisters if they had any siblings. They replied that they had a brother who was in his fourteenth year.

"Why did he not come with you to gather herbs?"

"Oh, he's a little slow and idiotic," the sisters

replied, and went on to discuss their brother's feeble nature.

"Oh please let him come with you next time you gather herbs. We would very much like to see him," said the other girls.

A short time later the Móafell sisters went to gather herbs again, and took Jón with them. They went to the same place, and this time there was a dense fog. Again they encountered the other two girls, who now asked if Jón could come home with them. They assured the sisters that nothing bad would happen to him, and added that they should not be concerned if he did not return home immediately. The two sisters agreed to let Jón go, particularly as he said he wanted to.

Time passed, and Jón did not return to Móafell. His disappearance was not common knowledge, until the Sunday prior to the beginning of Lent, when a boy dressed in fine attire arrived at Móafell. He went on to attend the church service planned for that day. When the minister began to examine the children the boy walked down the aisle to be questioned, and everyone in the church was astonished at how well he knew all the answers.

After that the boy vanished again, only to return to Móafell on the morning of Maundy Thursday. As before, he was dressed in fine clothes. He went to church, took the examination, and did well.

After the service, the boy asked the minister if he would confirm him. The minister was reluctant, as the boy had not attended church there. He also wished to know from whom the boy had his knowledge. In the end, he denied the boy his request. The boy then left the church, and did not stop at Móafell.

On Saturday before Easter, there was a knock at the door at Móafell. One of the sisters went to answer it. Outside she found one of the two girls from the valley, who asked if she and her sister could come early the following day to the field where they had originally met, wearing their best clothes.

Early on Easter Sunday the sisters put on their Sunday best and headed out to the pre-arranged location. The same girl appeared and asked them to accompany her across the river. They did, and soon arrived at a splendid farmstead and a church. They were led into the house, and received a very warm welcome. The girls from the field then revealed that they were the daughters of the minister there, and that Jón was to be confirmed later that day.

The Móafell sisters went to the church where a service and confirmation were taking place. There were many people in attendance, and their brother Jón was among the confirmation children. The sisters were unable to comprehend all that was said in the church, as a language different from their own was being spoken. They could see, however, that the service was Christian, and they heard the name of Jesus mentioned many times.

Following the service, their brother Jón told them that he would not be coming back to Móafell to live.

Several years passed. One day Jón returned to Móafell and invited his sisters and their mother to his wedding, saying that he was planning to marry one of the minister's daughters. The three women went to the wedding, which was both lovely and festive. After this, Jón never returned to the mortal world. And thus ends this story.

It is generally believed that many hidden people reside in Móafellsdalur and Tungudalur valleys. Both are uninhabited valleys in the Stífla area.

## NOTES

*The Lutheran confirmation, which took (and still takes) place when a child was in its fourteenth year, marked a child's transition into adulthood. The confirmation also served as the final examination for the child's education up to that point. Parents were required by law to teach their children to read and write, primarily so that they (the children) could better absorb the teachings of the church. This decree was enforced by the local minister, who would periodically show up at the farms and test the children to make sure their education was up to speed. This was a cause of great anxiety to many children and their families; if their educational development was judged to be lacking they could (and would) be removed from their parents and placed in foster care where their learning was more attentively seen to. In this story, the children are being tested in front of the whole congregation, presumably in anticipation of the big final exam.*

*I expect that no special allowance was given for learning disabilities in those days, so you can imagine what it was like for children who happened to be dyslexic, or who somehow deviated from the norm in their development. They must have been filled with anxiety every time the minister made an appearance to test them before the Big Day, terrified that he might remove them from their parents and place them in foster care.*

*That is why I find it fascinating in this story that the boy in question, who with his "feeble mind" apparently falls into this category, should be effectively removed from his home by elves, who take it upon themselves to educate him. Perhaps it was a subtle jab at the ruling authorities at the time, or perhaps this story falls into the category of child-abduction stories, in which grieving parents who had lost their children imagine them living with elves in circumstances far better than they, themselves, could have provided for them.*

# An elf woman is ferried across a river

The following incident took place in Bárðardalur valley some 20-30 years [prior to this story being recorded]. A girl from a farm on the west side of the river went to gather grasses and herbs on a heath on the east side of the river.

Close to the time when the girl was expected back, a woman was seen on the riverbank across from Halldórsstaðir farm. She called out, and this was heard by the farm people. The girl who had gone on the herb-gathering mission had been expected to call from the riverbank so that she could be fetched on horseback. When the woman was spotted on the riverbank it was believed that this was the girl who had gone to the heath. A woman willing to brave the river rapids was sent over with an extra horse to fetch her. She rode to where she could easily ford the river yet kept an eye on the girl on the opposite bank, thinking that she knew her.

She forded the river, still watching the girl, yet momentarily taking her eyes off her when she was almost across. Looking up again, she saw that the girl had vanished, which greatly surprised her. She looked all around, but the girl was nowhere to be seen.

Eventually she gave up trying to find her and rode over to Lundarbrekka farm to ask whether they had seen the girl, as she had been expected to stop there on her way back. The farm people told her that the girl she was looking for was still gathering herbs on the heath.

On discovering that her exertion and search had been in vain the woman went home, yet was astonished at her own delusion.

That night she dreamt that a woman came to her and humbly thanked her for ferrying her across the river. She told her that she had mounted the spare horse as soon as she had reached the eastern riverbank, and had remained there while the woman searched for the girl and until they had crossed over to the west side of the river. She asked the woman's forgiveness for all the trouble she had caused, adding that she had been in a great hurry to get across. She was from one of the hidden people farms in Lundabrekka and had given birth to a child out of wedlock. Her father had been furious and punished her harshly, so much that she had not been able to stay there. Thus she had fled to the west side the river to her relatives who lived at Sexhólagil, in front of Stóruvellir.

## NOTES

*As much as hidden people stories might be projections of the dreams, fantasies and yearnings of people trapped in difficult or painful circumstances, they could also be a reflection of people's sufferings. In this story the hidden girl has given birth to a child out of wedlock, and her father has punished her harshly. In the mortal world, having children out of wedlock was also subject to harsh punishment.*

*I cannot help thinking that by projecting their dreams, fantasies and sorrows onto the elf world, people created some sort of distance that helped them process the trauma and carry on. Here the hidden girl manages to find compassionate relatives who will take her in. Perhaps that was a fantasy of many a mortal girl or woman who unwittingly found herself "in the family way." Alas, I suspect that this sort of mercy did not happen very often in the mortal world, so this, too, might have been a fantasy for those who could not cope with their own cruel circumstances.*

# The brothers from Múlakot

In the early nineteenth century there were two brothers who lived at Múlakot in Fljótshlíð district, along with their mother. Their names were Jón and Ólafur.

One New Year's Day, before daybreak, Jón went to feed the lambs in the lamb shed. While he was there, a woman, well dressed and comely, appeared to him. She addressed him in a gentle voice, asking whether he would walk with her a short distance. He did not know her and was therefore wary, declining her request in a rather dry manner. Seeing that her strategy was not working she asked if he would marry her. Beginning to suspect that she was a hidden woman, he turned her down. She then asked him to have sexual relations with her, but he flatly refused, then hurried away and went home. She did not follow, and he did not tell anyone about this incident.

That same day he and his brother attended church at Teigur, in Fljótshlíð. On the way home they stopped to visit some of their neighbors, so it was late by the time they came to the river Merkjá, which runs near Múlakot.

The air was calm and though there were clouds it was not completely dark, since the moon was almost full. Just after crossing the river they saw a woman walking towards them, and when they met, Jón saw that it was the woman he had encountered in the lamb shed that morning.

She began asking Jón the same questions as earlier, and was very insistent. Jón became angry and tried to push her away, insulting her aggressively. His brother Ólafur placed himself between them, urging Jón to be calm. The woman was angry and remarked that even if Jón did not want to do her bidding he did not have to shove and degrade her. She added that he would get his just rewards later, as would all his offspring. Ólafur, on the other hand, having shown nothing but good conduct, would not be made to pay - he deserved more good than bad. She then left them, and vanished.

Some time later Jón married and moved to another farm. Soon he began to suffer from epileptic seizures. One of his daughters was born with such a weak constitution that she spent her entire life in bed with very limited awareness or knowledge of her surroundings. She never learned to speak, and died around twenty-five years of age. After her death, her sister began to suffer from a mental disorder that developed into full-blown insanity, despite previously having been a very promising young woman.

This man, Jón Árnason, last lived at Bakki in Austur-Landeyjar district, where he died. His son Loftur lived at Þorlaugargerði in the Westman Islands. He later became a Mormon and sailed to North America. Another son was named Árni and lived at Kirkjubær in the Westman Islands, where he died. His daughter is Sigríður, who married Jón Oddsson from Síða; they now live in Bakki and have many children. Einar Bjarnason, the district magistrate at Hrífunes in Skaftártungur district, married Jón's daughter Guðrún who went insane after her sister died; at that time she was still married to Einar.

## NOTES

*As I mentioned in the introduction, hidden people often appear as sexual predators in the old folk stories, which I find fascinating. Even more intriguing is how often hidden women are portrayed as sexual predators - powerful Valkyries*

*who know what they want and are not ashamed to ask for it. I also wonder at the man's reaction to the woman's advances. The first time she accosts him he simply walks away, whereas the second time - when someone else is present - he goes ballistic. It is like some element of shame has entered into the equation, and he is intent on degrading the woman in front of his brother.*

*In most translated stories of this nature, the last paragraph would probably have been left out, or at the very least edited. I decided to leave it in as-is, mostly because this reciting of names and lineage is so quintessentially Icelandic. Not to mention so quaint.*

# The woman in the mountain dairy

There once was a minister up north who fostered and raised a girl. The vicarage had a dairy up in the mountains where the minister kept his sheep and a cow during the summer. One woman acted as keeper of the dairy, and a number of shepherds were stationed there.

When the minister's foster daughter became old enough she was sent to be the keeper of the mountain dairy. She was a fine, pragmatic young woman of many talents, and she performed her work well in this instance, as in all others. She was considered an excellent prospect for a wife and received many proposals from eligible bachelors, but declined them all.

Eventually the minister sat down for a serious talk with his foster daughter. He urged her to marry, reminding her that he was getting on in years and would not always be there to support her. She remained impassive, saying only that she had no interest in marriage, that she was content as she was, and that she did not consider wedlock a prerequisite for happiness.

Winter came, and the people at the farm began to notice the girl's waistline expanding. In the spring her foster father once again had a talk with her, telling that she would not be going to the mountain dairy that summer since she was obviously with child.

The girl vehemently denied being pregnant, insisted that she felt perfectly fine, and told him she would most certainly be spending the summer in the mountain dairy, as before. Seeing that she was adamant about this, the minister gave up trying to persuade her. Instead he called a meeting with the shepherds who were going to be with her in the dairy and ordered them to keep her in their sights at all times. They gave him their word that they would. The group then went off to the dairy.

One evening, all the livestock went missing at once. Everyone in the dairy went out searching for it, except for the girl, who remained behind. A dense fog rendered the search both long and difficult, and the livestock was not found until early the next morning.

On returning to the dairy, the men found the girl

awake and unusually sprightly. They also noticed that her waistline had shrunk. They considered this very strange, as they had not thought pregnancy to be the cause of her weight gain.

In the autumn, all of them returned to the farm. It did not escape the attention of the minister that his foster daughter was narrower around the waist than she had been the winter before. He spoke to the shepherds, asking them if they had kept their promise. They confessed that they had left her alone on one occasion while they searched for the livestock. At this the minister grew furious. He railed at the shepherds, saying that he had suspected this would happen when he sent his daughter to the mountain dairy that spring.

A few weeks later a man came to the farm to ask for the girl's hand in marriage. She turned him down directly. Yet this time her foster father did not accept her refusal. Her suitor, he said, was reputed to be a fine man, and came from a good family. He had taken over his father's farm that spring and lived there with his mother.

And so, the wedding was arranged for the following spring, against the girl's will. The minister himself performed the ceremony. Prior to putting on her wedding attire, the daughter went to see to her future husband and said: "I have one request, seeing that all this was organized in opposition to my wishes. I ask that you never take in a winter laborer without speaking to me first, for otherwise I will not be an obedient wife to you." The bridegroom swore to her that he would not.

The wedding celebration over, the girl went to her new home and assumed the running of her husband's household. Yet she was decidedly melancholy in her new role, never happy or cheerful, even though her husband went out of his way to grant every one of her wishes and to spare her every exertion. Each summer, when the farm residents were out working in the fields, she remained at home. Her mother-in-law stayed with her for company and to help with the food preparations. When they were not cooking they were knitting or spinning, and the older woman told her daughter-in-law stories for her amusement.

Once, when the old woman had finished telling stories, she remarked to the girl that now it was her turn. The girl replied that she did not know any stories. The older woman pressed her, until the girl said she would tell her the only story she knew.

"There once was a girl who lived on a farm. She was the keeper of the mountain dairy. A short distance from the dairy there were large cliffs that she often passed. In the cliffs lived a hidden man, who was both fair and lovely. They soon became acquainted and formed a loving attachment. The man was so kind and generous to the girl that he never refused her anything and tried to please her in every way.

"Some time later it transpired that the girl was with child. The farmer for whom she worked confronted her about her condition when she was about to go to the dairy the following summer, yet she ended up going as usual. The farmer then asked the others who were staying in the dairy never to leave her on her own, and they promised that they would not. Even so, one night they all had to leave to go and search for the livestock when it went missing, and just then she went into labor. The man with whom she had been intimate came and stayed with her, tended to her at the birth, cut the umbilical cord, and bathed and swaddled the baby. Then he left with the boy, but not before handing her a glass from which to drink. That was the sweetest potion I have ..." just then she dropped her ball of wool on the floor, leaned down to fetch it and corrected herself, "... that she had ever tasted, I meant to say, so she was instantly healed from all her ailments.

"After that she and the hidden man never saw each other again. She was forced to marry another man against her wishes, and she so pined for her first lover that she never lived a happy day after that. And that's the end of this tale."

Her mother in law thanked her for the story and kept it in her memory.

Time passed uneventfully. The girl carried on in her unsociable manner, yet was kind to her husband.

One summer, well into the haymaking season, two men, one taller than the other, appeared before the farmer when he was out in one of his fields. Both wore large hoods so their faces were partly obscured. The taller of the two asked the farmer whether he had a place at the farm that he could offer them for the winter. The farmer said he would not take on any workers without his wife's consent, and that he would have to speak to her first before he could promise them a place.

The taller man then asked the farmer whether a distinguished man like himself was really so henpecked by his wife that he could not make such a trivial decision on his own. In the end it was agreed that the two men should have a place at the farm for the winter, even though the farmer had not consulted his wife.

That evening, the two strangers arrived at the farm. The farmer asked them to wait in one of the front rooms before going to his wife and telling her what had taken place. She grew furious and reminded him of the very first request she had made of him, which was now likely to be her last.

She added that since he alone had granted a place to the two men, he would also have to cope with the consequences of their winter sojourn.

Nothing more transpired until that autumn when the farmer and his wife were preparing to ride to church to take the sacrament. At that time it was common, as it is still in some places in Iceland, for those about to take the sacrament to go to each person at the farm, kiss them, and ask for their forgiveness for any trespasses they have committed against them. Up to that point the mistress of the house had managed to avoid the two winter laborers, and she had never allowed them to see her. This time was no different, and she did not bid them farewell.

As they were riding away from the homestead, the farmer asked his wife if she had taken leave of the winter laborers. She said that she had not.

He asked her kindly not to be so unscrupulous as to omit this.

"You were lacking in respect towards me when you admitted those men into our home without consulting me. Now I find the same thing happening again, as you wish to force me to embrace them. I shall obey you, yet you will see that my life hinges on this, and I think it likely that yours will too."

Having thus spoken she returned to the house.

She was gone so long that the farmer went inside to look for her. On entering the room of the winter laborers, he found his wife lying on the floor in the arms of the taller man. Both of them were dead, their hearts having burst with grief. The younger man stood above them weeping. A short while later he vanished, and no one knew where he went.

The story that the girl had told her mother-in-law was now recalled. It was commonly believed that the taller of the two laborers had been the hidden man with whom she had been intimate in the mountain dairy, and that the younger man, who had run away, had been their son.

## NOTES

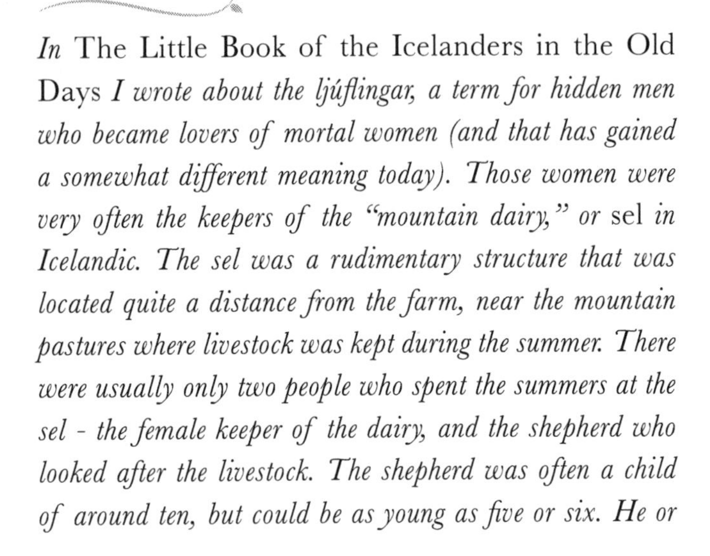

*In* The Little Book of the Icelanders in the Old Days *I wrote about the ljúflingar, a term for hidden men who became lovers of mortal women (and that has gained a somewhat different meaning today). Those women were very often the keepers of the "mountain dairy," or* sel *in Icelandic. The sel was a rudimentary structure that was located quite a distance from the farm, near the mountain pastures where livestock was kept during the summer. There were usually only two people who spent the summers at the sel - the female keeper of the dairy, and the shepherd who looked after the livestock. The shepherd was often a child of around ten, but could be as young as five or six. He or*

*she was responsible for driving the sheep to the pastures, watching over them, and then driving them back home in the evening so that the ewes could be milked. The dairy-keeper, called* matselja *("sel food woman") would then make butter or* skyr *(an Icelandic dairy product, somewhere between yogurt and cream cheese) out of the milk, which would be fetched by someone from the farm every few days. In this story there are more people in the sel, which indicates that the minister was relatively wealthy, like many people who were affiliated with the church in those days were.*

*Obviously the* matseljur *spent many days alone in the sel. Sometimes they came back pregnant at the end of the summer, and stories circulated that they had been involved in love affairs with hidden men. As I discussed in the introduction those stories probably reflected a deep longing for love, sex and romance that was denied to much of the population at that time, and might also have been used to explain away an unexpected pregnancy. Sometimes those women might have been raped. Or they might simply have been involved in an illicit love affair - as pretty much all love affairs were at that time. And, in keeping with Reverend Guðmundur's comments in "The ways of the hidden people," this romance between a hidden man and mortal woman ended tragically, as such entanglements (according to the stories) almost always did.*

# Two Christmas Eves

There was a farm where all the residents went to mass on Christmas Eve except one of the maidservants. When she had finished her work that evening she sat down on her bed, lit a candle, and began to read a book.

A short while later, two children came into the baðstofa and started playing. After a while they put their hands on the woman's lap. She took her candle, broke it into three pieces, gave each child a piece, and kept one for herself. The children were very glad, and ran off.

Presently a man in full dress entered the baðstofa. He greeted the woman and set about trying to seduce her. She refused his advances, and so he left.

Next a woman came into the baðstofa. She

greeted the maidservant and thanked her for her kindness to her children. Then she produced a red cloth and told her that she wished to give it to her in return for her warmth towards them, and also because she had rejected the advances of the man who had approached her. Then she left.

When the farm residents came home from church the mistress of the house saw the maidservant's red cloth and grew jealous. She tried to find out how it had come into her possession, but the maidservant refused to tell her.

Time passed, and the next Christmas arrived. The mistress of the house bid everyone go to church and remained at home by herself. When she had completed her domestic tasks she sat down on a bed with a candle and began reading a book.

Soon the same children as on the previous Christmas came into the baðstofa and began playing on the floor. When they placed their hands on the woman's lap she slapped them so hard that they ran off crying.

Next the man in full dress came in, greeted her kindly, and requested the same thing that he had from the maidservant. She thought that he must have been the one to give the maidservant the red cloth, and immediately complied with his wishes. He then left.

Now the same woman as before came into the room and took the mistress's right hand, saying that because she had spanked her children and caressed her husband with it, it would never be as good as before. At that, the mistress of the house lost all strength in her right hand.

## NOTES

*I don't think we need to dig deep to find the moral of this story:* Do not covet other people's belongings, slap their kids, or sleep with their husbands. THE END.

*I wanted to include it in this collection because it is one of many stories involving elves and Christmas Eve, and also because it is a variation on "The elf adornment." Happily, though, the fate of the woman who stays at home in this instance is not nearly as brutal as that of the women in the earlier story.*

# The hidden people's merchant

There once was a couple that lived up north. They had many children, yet despite this they lived a good life.

One summer's day, the farmer went to town on foot. His route took him along a long mountain road, and when he had gone a short distance he was caught in a fog so thick that he could not see the path in front of him.

He carried on a while, completely lost. Suddenly the fog lifted and he saw a man, very well dressed, coming towards him. They greeted each other, and the farmer asked the other man his name. He said that his name was Björgólfur and that he was a merchant, adding "on this occasion you shall do business with me."

The farmer was delighted with this proposition. The two walked on, and soon saw some imposing cliffs up ahead. Björgólfur headed in that direction, and on coming closer the farmer realized that the cliffs were, in fact, a splendid market town.

The farmer found the hidden people's merchant to be very amiable, and bought all he needed from him.

On leaving, he went to bid Björgólfur farewell. "You have not selected anything for your wife," the merchant remarked.

The farmer replied that he had nothing left with which to trade. Björgólfur then left, presently returning with an exquisite shawl and a quarter loaf of bread. "Give this to your wife to wear across her shoulders, and divide the bread between your children when you get home," he said.

The farmer thanked him for the gifts. Björgólfur then accompanied him on a distance, and they parted on the friendliest of terms.

The following summer the farmer returned to the same town and traded with Björgólfur. All transpired exactly as it had the summer before, with Björgólfur giving the farmer exactly the same gifts as previously.

That summer passed uneventfully. One day in

autumn, the farmer's wife was in the pantry when she heard a knock at the door. She went to open it and outside found Björgólfur who asked if she could come with him immediately as his wife was in great distress.

She went inside and told her husband who was at the door and for what reason. He instructed her to go immediately, "and take your scissors with you."

Björgólfur and the farmer's wife walked on until they came to his home in the market town. On arriving there the farmer's wife laid hands on Björgólfur's wife so that she was able to give birth. When the child was born Björgólfur left, returning with a jar of ointment. He told the farmer's wife to rub some of it into the child's eyes, "but take care," he said, "not to let it touch your own."

The woman's curiosity was aroused, so she briefly touched her right eye with one finger. She then bathed and swaddled the child before leaving. In parting, Björgólfur generously presented her with very fine gifts.

On her way home, the farmer's wife suddenly realised that she could see both into the ground and what was above it with the eye that the ointment had touched.

Time passed, and the following summer the farmer's wife wished to go to the town in which they had always traded in the past. The farmer made no objection.

When she arrived at the shop where she made her purchases, she saw Björgólfur standing behind the counter. She greeted him, saying, "So you are here?"

At that he was startled. He rushed at her and spat into her right eye. After that her vision was never as good on her right eye as on her left.

## NOTES

*In this story we have the motif of a man becoming lost in fog and emerging into a world infinitely better than the one he just left. Many Icelandic folk stories involve fog, probably because it struck dread in people's hearts. If you were caught in fog and became lost, you were lucky to get out alive. Fog is also symbolic of a transition from one place to another - from the mortal world to the hidden one.*

*From that common theme, the story segues into another well-known motif, that of the elf woman in a birth crisis. Here we also have an ointment that is applied to the eyes of the child, similar to what happens in "An elf woman in distress." In both cases the mortal woman gains the ability to see hidden people with the eye touched by the ointment. She recognises the hidden man in a market town, greets him, he responds angrily and retaliates by removing her ability to see him and other hidden people. In the case of the woman in "An elf woman in distress" this leads to a change in her fortune, as the inability to see the hidden people adversely impacts her life.*

*One thing I find curious here is that the elves apply ointment to their children's eyes presumably to allow them to see hidden people. In other words, their children are born with the* inability *to see their own kind. Which puts them in direct opposition to human babies, who according to the old folk stories were born* with *the ability to see hidden people, but needed to have that ability removed through the rinsing of their eyes with baptism water.*

# The minister's daughter

On the farm Prestbakki á Síðu in Skaftafellssýsla district there once lived a minister whose name was Einar. He was wealthy and had many children. He did not believe in hidden people and argued vehemently against their existence, daring them to show themselves if they were real. He often boasted that they did not have the courage to come to him.

One night he dreamed that a man appeared before him and said: "Here you see a hidden man as you have so often wished to see. You have spoken ill of us and dared us to find you. You fool - you believe you know things you cannot know of your own accord, and moreover you deny our existence. Well, from now on you shall not deny it because I am a hidden man, and as proof of this I shall take your eldest daughter away with me. You will never see her again."

Having thus spoken, he disappeared. The minister, when he awoke, thought that he saw the dreadful spirit of the hidden man glide away from his bed. He rose, only to discover that his twelve-year-old daughter had vanished. A large area was searched, yet the girl was not found.

Time went on, and the minister often thought about his own ignorance and the strange things that had come to pass. Then, on the following New Year's Eve, he dreamed that his daughter came to him. She was happy and told him that she was well. She said that she was allowed to come to him every New Year's Eve in a dream, but could not tell him about her circumstances except to say that everything she now heard and saw was very curious and strange.

Every New Year's Eve after that he dreamed that his daughter came to see him. At one point she told him that her foster father had died, after which his dreams of her became more frequent. During one dream she told him that she would be married the following morning to the son of an elf minister. After that, Einar never dreamed about his daughter again.

## NOTES

*Apparently being a doubter in the days of old was more than a little frowned upon, as is aptly demonstrated in this tale. I cannot help but think that it was circulated as a warning against bucking the system. "Attempting to disprove this folly with reason only makes things worse, for you will then be accused of belittling honorable men, as well as your ancestors and relatives, and turning them into liars," Rev. Guðmundur writes in "The ways of the hidden people." I think that about says it all.*

*On another level, this could easily have been a classic case of a child gone missing, and a grieving, guilt-ridden father fantasizing that* if only *he had believed in the existence of elves he could have prevented the tragedy of his daughter's disappearance. And, unable to cope with the loss, he dreams of her being alive and well in a hidden world parallel to his own.*

# Snotra the elf woman

There once was a man named Jón who lived at Nes, next to Borgarfjörður fjord. His wife's name was Snotra, and no one knew her family. She was an attractive and wise woman, with a calm and reserved manner. She and Jón had one daughter.

One thing in Snotra's behavior was considered odd: every Christmas Eve she disappeared, only to reappear on the eve of Christmas Day. No one wished to get involved in this affair, until one year when one of the farmer's shepherds decided to follow her.

When dusk fell on Christmas Eve, Snotra lay down to rest. A short while later she rose and left the house. She headed down to the sea, with the shepherd following at a distance. At the shore he watched as she took out two silk scarves, threw one on the ground, and covered her head with the other. Then she plunged headlong into the sea.

The shepherd did exactly as she had done, taking the silk scarf she had left behind and plunging into the sea after her. They glided downwards for a good while, until they arrived at green pastures. A short distance away the shepherd noticed an opulent city from which came the sounds of celebration and merriment. Snotra walked towards it and into a palace filled with people, where tables sagged from the sheer weight of all the food and drink on offer.

A man, dressed in fine attire, sat on a throne. He seemed despondent. On his right there was an empty seat. When Snotra entered, everyone in the room rejoiced, especially the man on the throne. He embraced her, and offered her the empty seat. The shepherd stood in the corner, hidden in shadow. Everyone began to eat, enjoying meat so fatty that the shepherd had never seen anything like it. Furtively he snuck over to a table and snatched some food, putting one rib into his pocket. When everyone had eaten their fill, joyous drinking and dancing began.

The following day, everyone who had been at

the celebration, including the shepherd, went to church. The shepherd found the singing beautiful, though he did not understand a word. The whole day was filled with gaiety, but towards evening, as Snotra prepared to leave, a hush fell over everything. When she left she bid farewell to the man on the throne with great sadness.

Snotra and the shepherd travelled the same way back through the sea, most likely upwards, until they came to the beach below Nes. On arriving there, Snotra noticed the shepherd and asked where he was going. He confessed that he had followed her. She replied that this was not possible. He then produced from his pocket the rib of mutton that he had taken from the table.

Seeing this, she realized that he was speaking the truth and said: "I wish to thank you most sincerely. I have been under a spell that forced me to spend my life in the mortal world, except for each Christmas Eve, when I could return to the elf world. The man you saw on the throne is a king, and he is my husband. Only one thing was able to lift the spell, and that was if a mortal man dared follow me and was able to see my home in the elf world. You have set me free, and now I can go home to my king. From now on you will become a man of great fortune. My mortal husband Jón will not live long, as he will grieve for me. I want to ask you to take our daughter and to treat her as if she were your own."

The shepherd promised to do this. Snotra then plunged back into the sea. He went home and told no one where he had been. What Snotra said came to pass - Jón did not live long after that. The shepherd took his daughter and remained at Nes until he was an old man. He enjoyed great fortune in his life. After this incident took place the farm was renamed, and is now called Snotrunes, after Snotra.

## NOTES

*At the beginning of this story, Snotra lies down to rest. This was customary in the old farmhouses during twilight in winter, when the light was too faint for people to see well and they therefore had difficulty getting any work done. Light sources were enormously precious at the time, and everything was done to conserve them. Hence people lay down to rest in the twilight, until it was completely dark and the light was formally lit.*

*One peculiarity of this story is that the elf world - which is splendid and prosperous, as usual - lies beneath the sea. This is vaguely reminiscent of H.C. Andersen's* The Little Mermaid, *about the woman who is under a spell in the mortal world and yearns to return to her own people beneath the sea. It also has very clear ties to the legend of the "Selkie" (not to be confused with "selfie") in Scottish, Irish and Faroese folklore, whereby seals were humans in seal guises and occasionally shed their seal skins on land. If a man found the seal body and hid it, the seal woman was doomed to become his wife. It is likely that the folk story of the "loved ones in the sea," which appears to have made the rounds in Europe, came to Iceland and merged with the local hidden people legend. Folklorists call this oikotypification, meaning the adaptation of a piece of folklore so that it fits the needs or expectations of a given society or community.*

# Ewes impregnated by elf rams

It happened shortly before Christmas on a farm in outer Hrútafjörður fjord that a shepherd noticed that three ewes were missing. It was evening, and a search for them was not possible since darkness had already fallen. Early the next day, however, they were back with the rest of the flock, so no more thought was given to this incident.

Mating season came, and those three ewes showed no sign of coming into heat. There was some concern that they might have come into contact with rams from other farms. Word was sent out asking whether anyone at the nearby farms had seen them, with or without rams, on that particular day. But no one had.

The ewes were soon discovered to be pregnant. The following spring, shortly before regular lambing season, two of them gave birth to white ewe lambs. The third ewe bore no lamb, and never did after that. One of the ewe lambs disappeared that spring, but the other one lived and grew large. It gave off a vast amount of wool, more than the farmer's other shearlings, so that in the spring the fleece weighed two and a half pounds after it had been washed and dried. This was considered very unusual, and therefore it was believed likely that the ewes had been impregnated by elf rams.

## NOTES

*As before, everything in the elf world is more prosperous and bountiful than in the mortal one. Even their shearlings give off more wool, and because the lamb in question gives off so much wool, it must have come from the elf world. Right?*

*Also, as if it were not enough for mortal women to have sex with hidden men, hidden women to prey on mortal men, hidden men to make advances towards mortal women, and hidden girls to give birth to children out of wedlock - here we have ewes from the mortal world being knocked up by hidden rams.* Is there no end to the debauchery?

# Þórunn and Þórður

This story begins with two farmers whose names were Bjarni and Björn. Bjarni had many children, whereas Björn had only one daughter. Her name was Þórunn. Björn was fairly poor, though he did earn enough to support himself.

It so happened that Bjarni passed away. The minister and district magistrate met to discuss what to do with the widow's children, for although she was rich there were too many of them for her to take care of. In the end the children were fostered out to farmers in the area, and their upkeep paid for. Björn offered to foster one of the boys, whose name was Þórður. Þórunn and Þórður were close in age, and were playmates.

Time passed, and both of them turned eighteen

years old. That summer, just before the haymaking season, Björn's wife asked him to send his workers out to gather herbs and to let the women from neighboring farms know so they could join them. She also said that Þórður and Þórunn should go on their behalf, along with the rest of their laborers.

The group headed out on twelve horses, rode along the valley, and then upwards out of it. The road went over a mountain pass, the sides of which were very steep so the procession was in single file. Þórunn rode last. When the group reached the top of the pass she was discovered to be missing, even though her horse was there with the reins around its neck. An extensive and thorough search was carried out, but Þórunn was not found.

Þórður was very much grieved at the loss of Þórunn, and often went out walking on his own. Þórunn's parents were likewise very upset by her disappearance.

A few years passed and Þórður became a shepherd on the farm. One autumn, all the sheep went missing. When it came close to Christmas Þórður asked for a new pair of shoes and some provisions. Björn's wife implored him to stay at home, but he said he would go, even if it meant that he would never return.

He set off and walked the whole day. That evening he found himself in a strange valley that he had not seen before. There he came to a very large hillock. Walking around it he discovered a stairway leading down. Descending the stairway he found a door, which he opened. Behind the door was a sheep. Looking closer, he saw that it was the leader sheep belonging to Björn, his foster father.

Þórður closed the house and walked further along the valley until he came to a stately farmstead. It had five gables, wood paneling on the north side, and three windows facing west. He went up to one of the windows and saw a man inside, clad in fine blue attire and an overcoat. The man was wiping tears from his eyes. Next he moved to the window in the middle and saw two men lying in bed. At the third window he saw a woman, with a younger woman sitting next to her. The older woman was wearing a traditional headdress and reading a book that he thought looked like the Bible.

Þórður Godded on the window, at which the young woman went downstairs and opened the door for him. She led him into a room and asked if he would like to eat before going to bed, since surely he was weary from his journey. Þórður asked to be shown to a bed, then undressed and lay down. When he had been lying there a short while the door opened and a woman came in. She greeted Þórður and asked whether he recognised her.

A stunned Þórður replied in the affirmative. She told him to be glad, and said: "When we parted a man came, took me to this valley, and married me. He is descended from elves, and he is the district magistrate here.

"I want to ask you, when you have slept a while, to rise from the bed and to go outside. There you will see a saddled horse. Mount it and ride along the valley. You will see a crowd of people, and in their midst a girl with a child. That girl is my husband's sister and she has had a child with her uncle. My husband is obliged to sentence her to death. That is why he was weeping earlier.

"When you arrive at the crowd of people you should urge your horse forward. The others will make room for you. Say to the girl: 'Would you like to mount the horse with me?' If she accepts, ride further down the valley with her. You will see a farm, and a woman standing at the door. This woman will invite the girl in, and you should let her go. When you have done this, I would ask that you return here."

The woman gave him a book and asked him to write this and everything else that transpired that winter in it, "for you shall have to remain here until the spring."

Þórður said that he had to get home to his foster father, for otherwise he would be presumed dead. The woman replied, "You will have to humor me in this instance."

Þórður went and did all the woman asked him to do. He then returned to the magistrate's farm. The magistrate was standing outside, and invited Þórður to come into the parlor. There they were served sheep hearts and lungs. As the woman placed them on the table she said: "I remember when we were together, dear Þórður, that you liked this type of food."

Þórður remained at the magistrate's home for the winter, and wrote everything that transpired in his book. The day before the First Day of Summer the woman told him to go home and take his foster father's sheep with him. "We have kept them fed all winter, for otherwise they would have perished. The winter has been harsh in my father's district. Nearly all the farmers have lost their sheep, and that is why we went and fetched his flock. You must come back here tomorrow and tell no one of your travels, but leave your book behind at my father's house."

Þórður set off. He arrived at Björn's farm and handed over the sheep, but did not speak a word to anyone of his travels, no matter how often they asked him where he had been. In the morning he woke early and asked his foster father to forgive him, for they would now have to part. Björn was upset, but Þórður said that he had to keep his word and promised to visit often.

Björn then said that he wanted to present Þórður with his inheritance, which was substantial. Þórður left, arriving late in the day at the magistrate's farm. The magistrate was waiting for him in the doorway, and bid him welcome. They went into the parlor, and when they had sat down Þórunn came in, leading her daughter by the hand. She walked over to Þórður and said: "I have no First Day of Summer gift to offer you, except my daughter." She placed her on his knee, and the magistrate took out a document that he handed to Þórður, saying: "This is for you. You can either become a farmer here, or accept a place as one of my farm workers."

Þórður thanked them for the gifts. He and the magistrate's daughter married and lived at the magistrate's estate until they were old.

And thus ends this story.

## NOTES

*In this story there are a number of points of significance.*

*First: what should be done with the widow's children. This is a passing reference to one of the most unjust and cruel practices in the Iceland of old, which is that when the man of the house died, the household was dissolved and the children fostered out to various farms. (To be fair, I have also heard of this happening when a woman died and a man was deemed unfit to keep his children, but this seems to have been far more rare.) Even when a widow was wealthy, as in this story, she was considered unable to take care of the household and children on her own. Someone from the district magistrate's office would turn up shortly after the funeral and auction off all of the household belongings. The widow was usually sent away to become a laborer somewhere while her children were scattered around the district. Even more devastating was the fact that the district paid a fee for each child or person fostered out, and this accumulated as a debt that the child or widow had to pay back. Despite the fact that people had done nothing to bring this cruel fate upon themselves, being a* niðursetningur, *as it was called, carried a huge amount of stigma. This was likely because such people were viewed as a burden to others, and to the district. Ostensibly the argument for this arrangement was that it would save people from becoming destitute, but the real reason was sometimes far more sinister: it allowed the church and crown to usurp the best land. Most Icelandic families today have ancestors who were subject to this cruel practice, including my own.*

Með nesti og nýja skó, *meaning: "A new pair of shoes and some provisions." This is a stock phrase in almost all Icelandic folk and fairy tales. In the Iceland of old, shoes were made of sheepskin, and were consequently very thin. Since poor people could not afford horses and went on most of their excursions on foot, a journey of any duration required more than one pair of shoes. So whenever anyone set off they had to take with them nesti (food, provisions) and nýja skó (new shoes, or a spare pair of shoes). Thus armed they could conquer almost anything - that is, if old stories are to be believed.*

*Then there is the leader sheep. The Icelandic sheep breed is believed to be unique in that occasionally certain sheep become the leaders of their flock. These animals appear to have a sixth sense about many things. For example if a flock was out in a pasture somewhere and the leader sheep showed a strong inclination to head home, the shepherd would almost always do so, since it usually meant that there was a storm coming. Leader sheep usually slept near the doors of the sheep shed, except when bad weather was approaching, at which they would move further into the shed. If a farmer or shepherd saw this he would not let his sheep out until the storm had blown over. Similarly, the leader sheep seemed to know where to tread even when there was a thick layer of snow on the ground. Parts of Iceland have highly dangerous crevices that can be obscured by snow in winter and that people and animals can easily fall into. The leader sheep seemed instinctively to know how to avoid those and would lead the way, not just for the flock, but also for the shepherd. These types of sheep were relatively rare, and it goes without saying that they usually fetched (and still fetch) a very high price for their owners - that is, if they were sold at all.*

*Now we come to the concept of "Godding on the window," which I am guessing is a tad foreign to most readers. When someone came to a farmhouse and it was dark outside, they did not knock at the door. This is because people were afraid of ghosts or other sinister creatures (see "The elf adornment" - I rest my case) knocking on the door at night. So instead of this, the arriving visitor would climb up on the turf roof, find a window, and call through it: "Here be God." This was called* Að guða á glugga, *or "to God on the window." At this the residents of the farm would know that a visitor had arrived, and that this visitor was of the mortal, rather than the spectral, variety. Because, as everyone knew back then, ghosts and other sinister creatures were not able to speak the word "God."*

*As I have discussed, the main room in most farmhouses was the baðstofa. However, the more stately farms, like the one mentioned in this story, had a separate room for receiving guests. This was the* stofa, *or parlor, and that is where Þórður was received when he had done the favor for the magistrate. Being invited to the stofa, rather than the baðstofa, was a gesture reserved for only the most distinguished guests.*

*The holiday known as First Day of Summer, which is mentioned in this story, came about because the old Icelandic calendar had only two seasons - summer and winter. As a testament to the vast importance of the summer season to the light- and warmth-starved Icelanders, the First Day of Summer was celebrated as a holiday. This even though it fell upon the first Thursday after the 18th of April each year, which in Iceland cannot constitute a real summer by any stretch of the imagination. The population would go to church on this day, and then give each other gifts. In that sense it was even more important than Christmas. One indication of its significance is that it is still observed as a public holiday today, and many people give each other First Day of Summer gifts. These are especially given to children, and are usually toys that can be played with outside, such as a ball or skipping rope.*

# The outlaw on Kiðuvallafjall mountain

Once in bygone days a man and his wife lived at the far end of a valley in the east of the country. Their names are not known, but they had a young daughter named Helga who was both fair and wholesome in appearance. The couple kept a hired hand named Jón, a loyal, hard-working young man with a keen mind who was well liked by all who knew him. Jón and Helga formed an attachment and fell in love. When Helga's parents learned of their mutual affection they opposed it, claiming that Jón was not a suitable husband for their daughter and, moreover, had neither security nor property. Yet under no circumstances did they want to lose him, for they prized his diligent and loyal nature. Thus they treated him well. Jón did not relinquish his position, for to do so would mean leaving Helga behind, and so he remained at the farm for many years. They continued to love one another, albeit chastely, and waited for an opportunity to be united.

At the furthest edge of the farm property was a valley named Kiðuvalladalur, after the Kiðuvellir plains that lay at one end. A great mountain named Kiðuvallafjall rose there. This was bounteous land where in spring and autumn livestock was put out to pasture. It was also very remote. One day when Jón was herding livestock down the mountain he heard a loud voice calling from somewhere further down, "Kiðuvalla, Kiðuvalla, alone I live on a mountain!" Jón was greatly perplexed, for he could see no one and there were no hiding places in the area. He concluded that he must have been mistaken and drove the livestock home.

The following day he was once again herding livestock on the mountain when he heard the call again in the same place, even more clearly than before: "Kiðuvalla, Kiðuvalla, alone I live on a mountain!" Jón thought the voice came from a large boulder and ran there but saw nothing. He sat down and all at once was seized with a curious intoxication and drowsiness, so that he fell asleep.

It then seemed to Jón as though a kindly stranger appeared before him, greeting him amiably. Jón returned the greeting and asked who the man was. "I am an outlaw," the apparition answered, "and I live inside this large boulder. I am the one you have twice heard calling. I did it to draw you to this place but I could not meet you, for I am on my deathbed. Today the boulder is not open but tomorrow when you come to do the herding it shall be. Meet me then." It seemed to Jón that he agreed to this. He then woke and drove the livestock home. Once there he told Helga all about the boulder-dweller. She replied that the man was surely in dire need and entreated Jón not to let him down. Jón promised to do all he could.

When he arrived at the boulder again it was open. Jón went in and found an ailing man lying on a bed of sheepskin. This was the same man who had appeared before him. He greeted Jón warmly and said, "You have done well to come. Soon my twelve-year stay here shall be over. I was sentenced to death for committing incest and fled here. I knew stone masonry; I took tools with me and carved out this stone, as well as other smaller ones in the area for storage. This one here has proven himself a most loyal ally," he added, pointing to a large, black dog that lay at his feet with its gaze fixed on its master. "This I ask of you, that you keep me company in my remaining hours," said the outlaw.

"Then I will run home and inform about my absence," answered Jón. The outlaw agreed.

Jón ran home and asked for leave to take a long journey. He was granted his request. When he returned to the boulder its occupant was still alive. He told Jón, "All my earthly belongings I bequeath to you, including this chest of money at my feet and the black dog, who shall prove a most valuable and devoted friend. I also ask that you bury me here, next to the boulder."

Jón promised to do so, and thanked the outlaw for the gifts. He then remained with him until he died. Jón prepared the body for burial and buried it next to the boulder as the outlaw had requested. After securing the black dog's affections he returned home and related all to Helga. He told her that they were now exceedingly wealthy, adding, "And let us now move to the boulder." They ran off secretly to the boulder and remained there until Helga's parents died; after that they returned to the farm and lived there until they were both very old. Thus ends this story.

In Brúaröræfi, in the Icelandic outback, is a valley named Kiðuvalladalur with a mountain rising high above it. That might be the location described in this tale.

## NOTES

*In the seventeenth and eighteenth centuries, the line between outlaw stories and hidden people stories began to blur. This is a good example of one such, where the outlaw lives inside a boulder, as the hidden people did. He also owns treasures, appears to Jón in a dream, and asks for help in his hour of need. Jón complies and helps him, with the result that his fortune changes. All of those motifs could have been lifted straight out of an elf story. On the other hand, the stranger in the story is most definitely an outlaw, and was banished from society for committing incest - one of the worst crimes in the Iceland of old.*

*In the days when this story took place, people were not allowed to establish their own home unless they owned the equivalent of three cows' worth, and if they were not able to establish their own home they were forbidden to marry. It took normal workers the better part of their lives to save up the required funds, and some never could. Consequently Jón and Helga had to love each other "chastely" until Jón came upon his unexpected windfall - though why they subsequently had to hide their good fortune from her parents is anyone's guess.*

# Ólöf of the mountain dairy

There once was a farmer's daughter named Ólöf, who lived with her parents. She was an attractive girl of many talents. She was of a marriageable age when this story took place, and was considered an excellent prospect for a wife.

One summer, Ólöf was sent to work in the mountain dairy of her father's farm. For much of the summer, Ólöf was alone in the dairy. One day a stranger arrived and asked her to give him some milk in a canister that he carried with him. Ólöf did so. Over the course of the summer the man came frequently to visit Ólöf in the dairy, and she gave him milk when he asked for it.

One day near the end of Ólöf's stay, the stranger came to see her again. He asked for the milk and she gave it to him as usual, yet remarked that she did not have much to give just then. He said: "Many a little makes a mickle, dear Ólöf." They then bid each other farewell. The stranger is not known to have visited Ólöf in the dairy again that summer.

The following summer Ólöf went back to the mountain dairy, and this time she was with child. As it happened, she went into a long and difficult labour while she was alone. In the midst of this crisis, the stranger from the previous summer appeared. He laid hands on her, and instantly she gave birth to a son. The stranger bathed the child and gave it every needed attention.

Ólöf was so weak from her labour that she was on the verge of dying. The stranger took out a glass jar with medicine and dripped some on her. Ólöf instantly felt better and within a short time had completely recovered. The stranger then left the mountain dairy, taking the child with him.

Time passed and no more was heard of Ólöf until it was reported that a good, respectable man had asked for her hand in marriage. Ólöf was indifferent to the proposal, saying she had no desire to marry at that time. Yet some time later she changed her mind, on the condition that her future husband would never allow a stranger to spend a night in their home without consulting her first.

The wedding took place, and Ólöf went to live with her husband at his farm. By all accounts their marriage was a harmonious one.

Several winters passed without incident. Then

one Saturday evening there was a knock at the door. The farmer opened it and found a stranger outside, along with an adolescent boy. The two greeted the farmer and the older man asked if they could spend the night. The farmer did not refuse, but said that he would have go into the house on his own first, and would return momentarily.

At this the visitor asked if he was so henpecked by his wife that could not make such a decision on his own. The farmer denied this. They exchanged a few words on the subject until the farmer could no longer withstand the jeering of the stranger. He invited him and the boy into the house.

They found Ólöf inside. When the visitors greeted her she flushed crimson, and did not utter a word. The farmer asked her to show the visitors to their seats, to which she replied that he could do so himself since he had been the one to invite them into the house.

The farmer offered them a seat on one of the beds. The older man stared at Ólöf as though mesmerised. "What are you staring at, fool?" she snapped. "My eyes take pleasure in what they see, as long as they see, my good woman," he responded. They are not known to have spoken to each other again that evening.

The following morning, Ólöf and her husband had planned to go to church and take communion, along with the farm workers. Before going to church it was customary for each person in the household to ask forgiveness for any wrongdoing towards another person, and the farm residents all complied with this custom.

As they were about to leave, the farmer asked Ólöf if she had apologised to the visitor for her inappropriate outburst towards him the previous day. She replied that she had not. The farmer asked her to go back inside and to make amends to the visitor. Ólöf was reluctant, but agreed when the farmer threatened to call off the church visit and communion if she did not do as he requested.

She returned to the house. Finding the stranger, she put both arms around his neck and asked him to not take offense at what she had said to him the previous evening. "There was a time when I would have been happier to see you," she added. They then clung to each other, and were racked with such grief that neither could utter a word.

They stayed that way until the farmer began to be annoyed at how long his wife was taking. He went inside to fetch her, and found her and the stranger with their arms around each other. Immediately he understood. The story has it that Ólöf and the stranger died in each other's arms at that very instant.

To the farmer, this incident was both strange and

tragic. He took the boy into his care and raised him. From him he learned that the stranger, his father, had been a hidden man, and that Ólöf had been his mother. However, that was all the boy knew about their relations.

The farmer had an elderly mother who lived with him, to whom Ólöf had once told the story of the hidden man and the girl in the mountain dairy. While relating the story of the medicine that was dripped on her while she was giving birth she had accidentally remarked: "It was the sweetest potion I ever tasted." Thus the old woman knew that Ólöf was speaking of herself. Apart from that Ólöf had kept silent about her involvement with the hidden man until the above incident came to pass. And thus ends this story.

## NOTES

*Astute readers will have realised well before the end of this story that it is the same as "The woman in the mountain dairy," only with a very slight variation. I decided to include it here as an illustration of how the stories could change when transmitted verbally. The earlier story, about the minister's daughter, is told in considerably more detail, whereas this one is almost a watered-down version of the other, as though told by someone who could not quite remember the original.*

# The hidden woman and the travellers

One fall it so happened that there were two men travelling together on foot. On their way from one farm to another they spotted a woman a distance away who was walking very slowly. One of the two men suggested that they might go to her, find out who she was, and ask whether she had any news to tell. The other man took this as a joke, yet the first one showed a serious intention to go and speak to the girl. His companion then began to tease him, saying that he could guess what his real motive was. At this they separated, the first man saying to his companion that he could wait for him while he talked to the girl if he so wished, or continue on to the farm and wait for him there.

The second man waited long enough to see his companion greet the girl and stand next to her for a few moments. He then glanced away, and when he looked back he saw no one.

The man continued on his way until he reached the farm. His companion did not arrive until late that evening, and once there he was met with much insinuation and jeering concerning his meeting with the girl. Most of it came from his companion, who knew of their conversation and the man's desire to meet with the stranger.

Not very long afterwards, the man who had ridiculed and teased his companion went mad and remained that way for the rest of his life.

As for the first man, the following Christmas Eve he put on his very best clothing to go out. There was a heavy blizzard and no weather for travelling, and when the man was asked where he was going he made no answer. He simply went on his way - to where, no one knew.

The snowfall remained heavy all through Christmas, and once it stopped the man returned. His clothes were just as dry and neat as they had been when he had taken them from his chest and put them on. No one knew where he had been during his absence. The rumor, however, was that the girl that he had met had been a hidden woman, and that he had spent Christmas with her.

Furthermore, it was supposed that she had caused his erstwhile companion to go mad, as payback for his ridicule and jest.

## NOTES

*In this story, the man who suggests intercepting the girl says that he wants to find out if she has any news. Not any particular news, just ... news. This clearly speaks of the isolation on the farms back then, when weeks or months could go by without anyone coming with any news from other parts of the country, to say nothing of the world. Small wonder that people thirsted for news. Though whether their lives were any poorer for it than ours today, with our glut of news and information, is open to debate.*

*When the man returns to the farm after his sojourn over Christmas, it is especially noted that his clothes were* dry. *Indeed, this must have been a strange occurrence, since one could hardly go outside in Iceland without becoming wet in those days. Obviously, then, it must have been very uncomfortable to have been a traveller, and easy to catch hypothermia. It also shows us just how important the Icelandic sheep was, as wool is a material that keeps people warm, even when it is wet. I have heard it said that the Icelandic sheep ensured the survival of the Icelandic people through the centuries, and have no doubt that it is true.*

# Kristín from Hof

Late in the 18th century, there lived a woman named Kristín who grew up on the farm Hof, on Höfðaströnd. She desperately wanted to see a hidden person.

On one occasion, Kristín was out searching for some sheep. She lay down to rest on a mountain slope, and fell asleep next to a large boulder. She dreamed that a woman both young and pretty came to her and said: "You have long wanted to see us, and now you see one of us here; I went to gather your sheep up on the knoll, and they are now coming down the slope just above the boulder." Having thus spoken, the woman vanished into the boulder, and Kristín awoke to see her sheep coming down the slope.

Time passed, and Kristín became a laborer on a

farm. One evening, warm milk was being rationed out for dinner. Kristín often kept her dinner for later. That night she dreamed that a woman came to her with a small wooden container and asked Kristín to give her some milk. Kristín believed that she recognized the same hidden woman that at one time had fetched her sheep for her. She poured some milk from her *askur* into the wooden container, and told the hidden woman that she could take food from her askur whenever she wished. The hidden woman thanked her, and told her that she could mention her name if she was ever in need of anything.

That summer, the milk often disappeared from Kristín's askur, as the hidden woman fetched it during the night.

A few more years passed. By this time Kristín had developed a tumor that had grown very large. One evening she thought to herself that it might be a good idea to try to call the hidden woman. Out loud she said: "I wish my dear hidden woman was here to help me."

Kristín slept soundly through the night. On waking the next morning she felt something cold next to her cheek. It was a round glass jar containing something brilliantly red, about the same consistency as syrup. She was delighted to discover this, as she was convinced that the hidden woman had sent it so that she could apply it to her tumor. This she did, once a day for two weeks. By the end of that time the tumor had disappeared, and the ointment was gone from the glass jar. Kristín kept the jar safe among her possessions for the rest of her life.

## NOTES

*A word that is probably unfamiliar to foreign readers: askur. This was a wooden bowl with an attached lid (on hinges), and each person owned one. At mealtimes, the mistress of the house doled out food to the farm residents, which would go into their askur. They would then eat their food immediately, or keep it for later, as they chose. On some farms, in fact, food was rationed out only once a week, and each person would be responsible for making their ration last.*

*Some* askar *(plural of askur) were veritable works of art, intricately carved with ornate patterns and sometimes the owner's initials on them. Today many Icelanders make a rather unpleasant association between askar and disease, since in the old days the dogs were usually allowed to lick the askar clean. Naturally this gave rise to some gruesome illnesses, including a large part of the population contracting tapeworm. Indeed, the somewhat ambivalent relationship that many Icelanders have with dogs today is frequently explained by this association, which still lives on in the minds of many people, subconsciously if not consciously.*

# The hidden woman at Fossar

From 1756 to 1766 a couple resided at the farm Fossar in Svartárdalur valley. The farmer's name was Halldór, and his wife's name was Helga. They had two sons; one named Árni, who was seven, and the other named Jón, who was six.

Just south of the farmyard there was a gravel hillock, or ridge, that extended towards a small river. On one part of the ridge there was a bluff with a sheer drop down to the water. The two boys liked to roll rocks from the edge of the drop, as there was a pool below and the rocks made a splash as they fell into it.

Their mother had a habit of lying down to rest

when she had finished her morning chores. One day, just after falling asleep, she thought that a woman came to her wearing a black cloak with a high headpiece like those on the Icelandic national costume. The woman was of average height and rather corpulent. Helga guessed her to be of middle age. She had a forceful presence and seemed angry, as she said: “I would ask you, good woman, to take better care of your sons and not to let them roll rocks around my home and drive my children mad with fright.” Then she left.

Helga awoke and believed that she saw the woman leaving. She got out of bed and thought to herself that this was mere folly, as she hated all forms of superstition. Yet, being a woman of sharp mind, she went outside and saw her two boys merrily rolling rocks off the hillock into the river. She forbade them to continue with their game, giving them the reason that they could easily fall into the water after the rocks. She then made them return to the house with her.

A couple of days passed, two or three - I don’t recall, and again Helga had lain down to rest as usual. She dreamed that the same woman came to her again, even more angry than before, so that Helga was now afraid of her. The woman said: “Your boys are still troubling me and my children, and you will be sorry if you do not make them stop." She then left. Helga awoke with a start, went outside, and saw her two boys rolling rocks into the water, as before. She called to them brusquely, promising them a thrashing if she caught them doing it again. She then ordered them back to the house.

Three days later she once again lay down to rest. Just as she was about to fall asleep she heard someone enter the baðstofa and say to her abruptly: "Helga, go outside and find your boys." Nothing else was said.

She rose hastily to her feet and went outside. There she saw the younger boy standing on the hillock, and the other one lying next to him. She went to them and seized hold of the one lying down, telling him to get up now, or he would regret it. But his body was limp and he was unable to speak. She carried him home, whilst giving the other boy a scolding.

Árni lived for four more days, and on the fifth day he died, as limp and mute as he had been when Helga found him on the hillock. Jón, on the other hand, grew into a strong and prosperous man. He had three children, one of whom is still alive.

## NOTES

*In my understanding, this story is a fable designed to warn children about the risks of certain behaviors. Here the boys are hurling rocks into the river from a very dangerous spot. It is easy to imagine someone constructing a story to warn children that, if they did not obey their mothers and stay clear of dangers, a terrible fate could befall them. Clearly the threat of falling into an ice-cold river was not enough - whoever cooked this up decided to haul out the heavy ammunition:* death by elf.

*This story thus makes abundantly clear that Icelandic elves were badass, and not of the airy-fairy, flit-among-the-flowers variety. And so, I rest my case.*

# In closing

I do hope that you have enjoyed this collection of stories about the hidden people, and my ruminations on their meaning in the grand scheme of things. If you did I would be enormously grateful if you would take a few minutes to post a review on Amazon, Goodreads, or wherever you share your love of books. Reader reviews are so important for indie authors, and your support would be deeply appreciated. For more on the Icelanders of old and their weird and wonderful beliefs, you might enjoy *The Little Book of the Icelanders in the Old Days* and *Icelandic Folk Legends*, both of which are available through Amazon.

# Acknowledgements

Huge thanks to everyone who helped put this book together. First, to my wonderful husband Erlingur Páll Ingvarsson, for designing the interior and cover and generally for being an invaluable part of the production process. Also to the five people who acted as beta readers and provided me with some excellent input: Amy Clifton, David Zell, Jon Ofjord, Mary Heneghan, Mary Lokken and Mikael Fernstrom. Also to Aðalheiður Guðmundsdóttir at the Folkloristics department at the University of Iceland, who swiftly and very good-naturedly responded to my questions about some of the more bizarre aspects of these stories.

# ABOUT THE AUTHOR

Alda Sigmundsdóttir is a writer, journalist and translator. She holds a degree in English and Folkloristics and is the author of seven other books about Iceland:

*The Little Book of Tourists in Iceland*
*The Little Book of Icelandic*
*The Little Book of the Icelanders*
*The Little Book of the Icelanders in the Old Days*
*Icelandic Folk Legends*
*Unraveled*
*Living Inside the Meltdown*

In addition, Alda has written extensively about Iceland for the international media, and regularly gives talks and lectures on contemporary and historical Iceland. Catch up with Alda on her website aldasigmunds.com, where you can also sign up for her monthly newsletter, or find her on Facebook, Twitter or Instagram.

# Sources

*Árnason, Jón, comp.* Þjóðsögur Jóns Árnasonar/ *The Folk Tales of Jón Árnason. Reykjavík: n.p., 1954-1961. Print.*

*Jónasson, Jónas, and Einar Ól. Sveinsson.* Íslenzkir þjóðhættir *[Icelandic Folkways]. 4th ed. Reykjavík: Opna, 2010. Print.*

*Ólafsdóttir, Sólveig. Hólavallagarður, Gamli Kirkjugarðurinn Við Suðurgötu. Diss. Bifröst U, 2009. N.p.: n.p., n.d. Print.*

*Sigmundsdóttir, Alda.* The Little Book of the Icelanders in the Old Days. *Reykjavík: Enska Textasmidjan, 2014. Print.*

THE LITTLE BOOK OF THE HIDDEN PEOPLE



Enska textasmidjan
Reykjavík, 2015

Layout and cover design: Erlingur Páll Ingvarsson



ISBN 978-9935-9248-7-2

LITTLE BOOKS
PUBLISHING

Made in the USA
Lexington, KY
28 June 2018